POKÉMON TRAINER FILE

NAME:

AGE:

POKÉMON BUDDY:

First published in Great Britain 2022 by Farshore
An imprint of HarperCollins*Publishers*
1 London Bridge Street, London SE1 9GF
www.farshore.co.uk

HarperCollins*Publishers*
1st Floor, Watermarque Building, Ringsend Road
Dublin 4, Ireland

ISBN 978 0 0085 0767 1
Printed in Romania
1

A CIP catalogue record for this title is available from the British Library.

Parental guidance is advised for all craft and colouring activities. Always ask an adult to help
when using glue, paint and scissors. Wear protective clothing and cover surfaces to avoid staining. Adult supervision
is advised for the recipe activity within the book. Always ask an adult to help when using sharp implements.

Stay safe online. Farshore is not responsible for content hosted by third parties.

MIX
Paper from
responsible sources
FSC™ C007454

FSC
www.fsc.org

This book is produced from independently certified FSC™ paper
to ensure responsible forest management.

For more information visit: www.harpercollins.co.uk/green

ANNUAL 2023

CONTENTS

THE JOURNEY STARTS TODAY!

HEY TRAINER, ARE YOU READY TO CATCH SOME POKÉMON?

Come with Ash and his buddy Pikachu as they explore Galar – the latest known region in the world of Pokémon – and beyond. Along with friends Goh and Chloe, Ash is all fired up to discover new Pokémon data and build his Trainer knowledge.

In this Annual, you can join the gang and take your own Trainer skills up a level. Learn from the best in the incredible stories, scan through recently discovered Pokémon in the A-Z, and find out if you're Master Trainer material in the puzzles.

LET'S GET STARTED!

IT'S ALL ABOUT MEW

Goh is determined to catch the Mythical Pokémon Mew.
Can you help him try?

Mew pops up 8 times in this book. Stay alert and write the page numbers where you spot Mew in the boxes below.

ANSWERS ON PAGE 68

TRAINING WITH ASH

Show off your moves in these awesome challenges!

NAME: *Ash Ketchum*

POKÉMON BUDDY: *Pikachu*

AGE: *10*
FROM: *Pallet Town, Kanto*

CURRENTLY IN:
Vermillion City, Kanto

Ash is a brave Pokémon Trainer who loves to battle. He works at the Cerise Laboratory as a research assistant and dreams of becoming the world's greatest Pokémon Master.

WHO'S THAT POKÉMON?

Professor Cerise has sent Ash to spot Pokémon in the Galar region. Which Pokémon does he see? **Match each name to its close-up picture.**

BUTTERFREE   NICKIT   STUNFISK   ZIGZAGOON

A

B

C

D

ANSWERS ON PAGE 68

POKÉ BALL - GO!

Help Ash race through the maze to his buddy Pikachu.
How many Pokémon can you catch along the way?

◀ **START**

FINISH

Did you pass these Pokémon?
Complete their names to add them to your Pokédex!

1. K _ _ _ F _

2. _ _ RF _ _ _ CH' _

3. _ RA _ OV _ _ _

4. _ ON _ T _

5. SK _ O _ _ _ T

6. _ _ _ _ VI _ _ IGHT

ANSWERS ON PAGE 68

SPARK A FRIENDSHIP

Which Electric-type Pokemon will be your buddy?
Follow the flowchart to find out!

START

Are you more like **Ash** or **Goh**?

PIKA-PIKA!

Can you spot Pikachu hiding somewhere on these pages?

Are dogs your favourite animals?

ASH

JOLTIK

YES

NO

YAMPER

ALWAYS

Do you like to be in charge?

TOXEL

NOT REALLY

BATTLE

CATCH

Is it more fun to **catch** Pokémon or **battle**?

10

CHARJABUG

YES

JOLTEON

GOH

Are you the best at telling jokes?

ALOLA

KANTO

RAICHU

Play **video games** or watch **anime**?

NO

GAMES

ENERGETIC

ANIME

Kanto or **Alola** region?

CHILLED

SCORBUNNY

Scorbunny or Grookey?

GROOKEY

Are you **chilled** out or **energetic**?

READY TO GOH!

Perfect your research skills to stay a step ahead!

NAME: *Goh*

POKÉMON BUDDY: *Goh's first partner was a Scorbunny, which evolved into a Raboot, then a Cinderace.*

AGE: *10*   **FROM:** *Vermillion City, Kanto*

Goh loves studying Pokémon and dreams of one day catching Mew. He works with Ash at the Cerise Laboratory, and his ultimate goal is to complete his Pokédex.

HIDE 'N' SNEAK

If you want to catch it, you gotta spot it first!
Unscramble the names of the Pokémon and then draw a line to locate them in the picture.

WEELTCH

_____

AREECMIL

_____

AWDDREN

_____

ORCHSKITENC

_____

RESREPREKR

_____

BUYNNROCS

_____

ANSWERS ON PAGE 68

TIP

Scan through the A-Z if you get stuck on the names.

PIXEL PUZZLE

Uh-oh, Goh's Rotom Phone is playing up.
Which Pokémon is he trying to identify?

1 _____

2 _____

3 _____

START

P E C P K E R **R** B **C** L S I C O N R B D I V E S A R Y A A

_____

IN A SPIN

Goh says the best way to catch is to throw a curveball! **Circle every third letter to reveal who is in the Poké Ball.**

ANSWERS ON PAGE 68

GIGANTAMAX WORDSEARCH

It's time for some serious searching in Galar.
How many Pokémon can you find hiding in the grid?
Spot them to add them to your Pokédex!

D	C	X	A	L	R	O	N	S	S	S	R	S	F	D
I	M	R	.	M	I	M	C	C	U	P	G	A	R	
M	X	S	S	E	H	N	A	E	F	.	B	L	E	
R	A	X	S	N	O	R	L	A	X	A	P	I	E	
L	L	P	V	O	K	F	V	H	H	V	H	N	P	
I	R	D	Q	O	I	E	X	I	D	U	S	K	Y	
N	O	T	L	S	I	A	S	M	R	O	I	S	D	
E	N	S	S	L	N	D	P	A	Q	V	V	T		
H	S	O	C	P	O	X	Y	I	G	G	O	K	E	
X	G	U	O	R	I	A	N	D	A	U	T	U	R	
B	E	N	L	N	H	L	Y	I	P	B	C	F	S	
E	S	A	O	B	H	R	H	M	U	P	R	X	N	
Q	X	P	Q	V	.	Q	Q	P	L	I	A	M	E	
D	T	V	K	M	X	N	Q	D	T	L	B	C	P	
N	E	P	L	C	N	S	C	S	I	B	M	U	K	
T	K	S	C	O	R	V	I	S	Q	U	I	R	E	

Can you find the special Poké Ball
letters throughout the grid?
**Write the letters here and unscramble
them to catch a Gigantic Pokémon!**

_ _ _ _ _ _ _ _

Word Search

ARCTOVISH · DREEPY · MEOWTH · SANDACONDA
BLIPBUG · EISCUE · MR. MIME · SNOM
CARKOL · FALINKS · NICKIT · THIEVUL
CORVISQUIRE · GOSSIFLEUR · RAPIDASH · TOXEL
DRAGAPULT · IMPIDIMP · RILLABOOM · WOOLOO

I	I	I	U	.	C	W	K	R	S	B	X	V	T
X	A	L	R	O	N	S	W	A	T	V	A	I	D
E	P	A	S	A	V	V	N	O	M	W	K	H	W
N	N	S	N	I	V	D	X	I	O	C	V	T	T
M	S	T	U	S	A	E	E	O	I	L	M	W	C
I	H	N	M	C	L	M	L	N	U	H	P	U	T
E	L	S	O	N	A	O	I	M	.	D	R	E	R
S	C	N	A	R	O	P	E	V	L	R	I	M	X
B	D	X	O	D	L	M	X	U	U	S	L	U	A
A	E	D	I	A	I	A	P	N	V	S	L	W	L
E	W	V	U	M	P	P	X	.	E	C	A	V	R
I	X	B	.	H	L	.	A	C	I	K	B	X	O
H	G	R	.	E	U	O	E	R	H	M	O	.	N
S	M	O	S	J	M	E	O	W	T	H	O	I	S
S	N	O	M	V	P	W	N	P	A	K	M	L	B
O	I	H	X	A	L	P	O	N	S	I	J	T	L

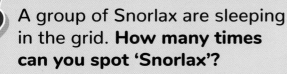

? A group of Snorlax are sleeping in the grid. **How many times can you spot 'Snorlax'?**

ANSWERS ON PAGE 68

TOUGHING IT OUT!

THIS IS ANOTHER CHAPTER IN THE STORY OF ASH AND GOH'S ADVENTURE-FILLED JOURNEY THROUGH THE WORLD OF POKÉMON!

Ash and Goh were carrying out special training with two of their Pokémon, Riolu and Farfetch'd, when Professor Cerise arrived with a surprise. "I've got a present for you two," he said. "Tickets to an official World Coronation Series Master Class battle!"

"Are you saying we get to see Leon battle?" Ash asked, amazed. Leon was his hero – the number one, undefeated Pokémon Trainer in Galar. "You've got it!" said Professor Cerise.

On the night of the battle, Leon went up against Raihan, a Dragon-type Gym Leader of the Galar region. It was a one-on-one match – they could only use one Pokémon each.

Ash's Riolu and Goh's Farfetch'd wanted to watch the battle, too. Everyone was psyched!

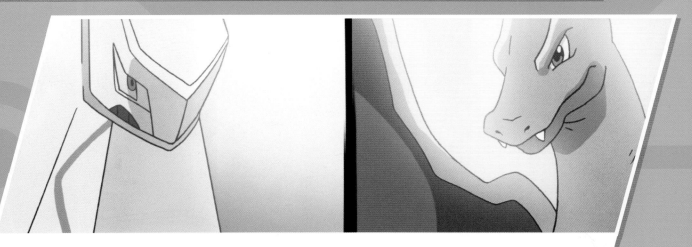

The announcer's voice boomed around the stadium. "Raihan brings out Duraludon! And Leon has chosen his undisputed ace, Charizard!"
Goh looked up Duraludon on his Rotom Phone. It was an Alloy Pokémon – a Steel- and Dragon-type with a metallic body. A fearsome opponent for Leon and Charizard.

The battle commenced, and it was an evenly matched fight. Duraludon used Metal Claw and Charizard used Dragon Claw to counter it. Duraludon used Steel Beam – converting energy in its body to release vast amounts of power. Charizard countered it with Flame Thrower. A mighty clash!

"And Steel Beam wins that clash!" the announcer called. "But even so, Charizard is still on its feet!"

"I offer you thanks," said Leon to his opponent. "Because of you two, Charizard's fighting spirit is fiery-hot!"

Raihan responded by summoning Gigantamax Duraludon. Leon did the same with Charizard. Now it was a battle between two humongous Pokémon!

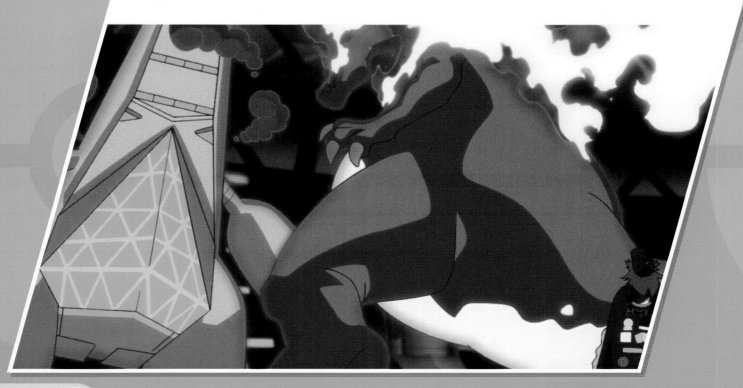

Gigantamax Duraludon was strong, but still no match for Leon and Gigantamax Charizard. With one final move, Duraludon was left unable to battle, and so the win went to Leon!

"My goal is to work with the Trainers in my Gym to hone my skills and challenge you again," Raihan told Leon. "Because it truly is my quest to break your unbeaten record once and for all."

Suddenly, Ash jumped to his feet. "No, that's my job!" he yelled at the top of his voice. "I'm gonna beat Leon and become the greatest Pokémon Trainer who ever lived, you'll see!"

Leon smiled. "Sure! I'll be waiting!"

The next day, Ash and Goh were admiring a huge statue. They asked a girl who was sitting nearby, "Is this statue supposed to be Leon?" "No, not a chance!" she replied. "That's a famous Galar-region hero."
The girl's name was Sonia, and she was doing research for her gran, a Pokémon Professor. Sonia went on to explain that long ago, a great black storm covered the Galar region. The land was assaulted by gigantic Pokémon, but they were defeated by a single young hero bearing a sword and shield. The statue was meant to depict the young hero.

"How cool is that?!" Ash and Goh exclaimed.

Just then, a Trainer passed by, holding an injured Pokémon and looking worried. Ash asked him what was wrong.
"There's a bridge over there with this huge, weird ... aw, man ..."
the Trainer trailed off and rushed away to the Pokémon Centre to find help.
"Let's check it out!" Ash and Goh said together. They ran towards the bridge.

At first, Ash and Goh couldn't see anything strange. But suddenly, a Farfetch'd appeared. It was similar to Goh's Farfetch'd from Kanto, but it was carrying a huge leek! They quickly scanned it on the Rotom Phone.

"The Wild Duck Pokémon. A Fighting-type," the Rotom Phone said. "Farfetch'd always carries a leek that is twice as long and heavy as its own body, and never lets go. This is the Galarian form of Farfetch'd."
"I've got this!" yelled Goh, and he tried to catch the Galarian Farfetch'd with his Poké Ball. But it wanted to battle. Goh summoned his Kantonian Farfetch'd.

"All right!" yelled Ash.
"A Kantonian and Galarian battle!"

21

The Galarian Farfetch'd beat the Kantonian one with just one attack, and then wanted to battle again. Before Ash could summon a Pokémon, Riolu came out of the Poké Ball, ready for a fight.

"Riolu! Out on your own?" Ash was surprised. "I see. You wanna battle!" Riolu battled the Galarian Farfetch'd and did a better job than the Kantonian Farfetch'd had done. Ash and Riolu used some new moves from their special training, including the Double Team move that made Riolu multiply.

But then, the Galarian Farfetch'd used an immense move called Brutal Swing. "Riolu's wiped out, Ash," said Goh. "Riolu hasn't given up yet," Ash replied. "So, I'll just believe in Riolu!" The Galarian Farfetch'd didn't want to give up, either. They were both loving the battle!

It was soon clear that the battling Pokémon needed a bit of recovery time. The whole gang headed to the Pokémon Centre.
"The Pokémon you brought are all feeling just fine," said Nurse Joy.

The Galarian Farfetch'd looked like he was ready to battle again.
"You really do love battling, don't you?" said Ash. "I've got an idea. How about you come with us? Come with Riolu and Pikachu and get strong. Like a family!"
The Galarian Farfetch'd agreed. "I just caught a Galarian Farfetch'd!" Ash exclaimed with excitement.

ASH HAS MADE A NEW FRIEND IN THE GALAR REGION. BUT WHO KNOWS WHEN HE MIGHT BE ABLE TO BATTLE LEON? GOH DIDN'T CATCH ANY POKÉMON THIS TIME. WILL HE BE ABLE TO CATCH ANY MORE GALAR POKÉMON?

ADVENTURES WITH CHLOE

Put your skills to use in these training tests!

NAME: *Chloe Cerise*

POKÉMON BUDDY: *Chloe's family pet is a Yamper, and her first Pokémon was an Eevee.*

AGE: *10*   **FROM:** *Vermillion City, Kanto*

Chloe is the daughter of Professor Cerise, the head of the Cerise Laboratory. She was nervous around new Pokémon at first, but now she, too, has become a Pokémon Trainer.

RACE TO THE RAPIDASH

Chloe is rushing to help an injured Rapidash in the Galar region. **Use the key to follow the quickest trail.**

KEY

Follow the squares in this order

START ▶

FINISH ▲

ANSWER ON PAGE 68

PLAY WITH YAMPER

Can you draw Chloe's family Pokémon, Yamper?
Use the grid as a guide, then colour in your picture.

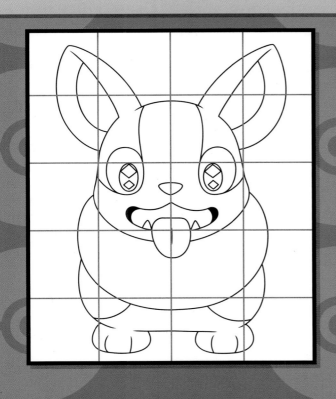

EVOLVED OR NOT?

Which of these Pokémon is NOT an evolved form of Chloe's partner, Eevee?
Circle your answer.

SYLVEON	UMBREON	VAPOREON
LEAFEON	ESPEON	FLAREON
GLACEON	INTELEON	JOLTEON

ANSWER ON PAGE 68

LET'S CATCH SOME POKÉMON!

It's time for some friendly competition! **Grab a dice and a second player and see who can catch the most Pokémon.**

WHAT TO DO:

- Choose which player will be Ash and who will be Goh.

- The youngest player starts. Begin with Challenge 1 and take turns to roll the dice.

- Whatever number the dice lands on, circle that Pokémon on your challenge card – now it's caught!

- If you land on the same number twice, it's a miss and the other player takes their turn.

- Keep going until one player has caught all the Pokémon on their card. They win the challenge!

WHO'S THE CHAMPION?

Count up who won the most challenges. **Is Ash or Goh the overall winner?**

THE CHAMPION IS _____ , PLAYED BY _____ .

THEY CAUGHT [ ] POKÉMON IN TOTAL.

GO, GO GRASS TYPES!

Goh thinks he knows everything there is to know about Grass-type Pokémon! **Show him you can complete the Evolution chains by adding the correct name to each blank space.**

LOTAD   THWACKEY   BULBASAUR   LOMBRE   APPLETUN

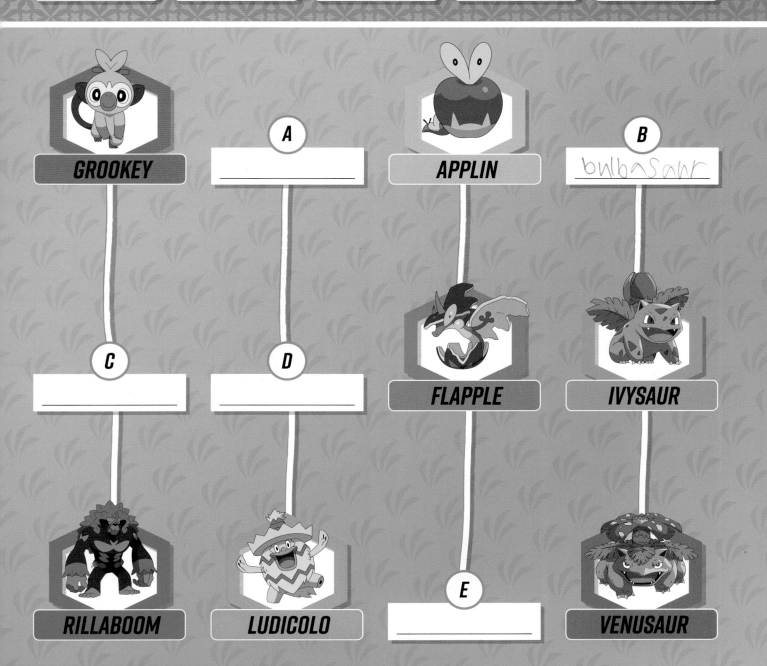

GROOKEY

A _____

APPLIN

B bulbasaur

C _____

D _____

FLAPPLE

IVYSAUR

RILLABOOM

LUDICOLO

E _____

VENUSAUR

ANSWERS ON PAGE 68

POKÉDEX A-Z

Ash and Goh make an awesome research team! They're making lots of new discoveries on their adventures in Galar, and all the data is logged on their Rotom Phones.

These are Pokemon that Ash and Goh have run into while travelling across several regions. This is not all of them, and some are just ones they HOPE to run into!

Which one would you most love to catch?

Rotom, please show me your data!

29

ALCREMIE

FAIRY
0.3 m
0.5 kg

ABOUT:

When it trusts a Trainer, it will treat them to berries it's decorated with cream.

APPLETUN

GRASS · DRAGON
0.4 m
13.0 kg

ABOUT:

Its body is covered in sweet nectar, and the skin on its back is especially yummy. Children used to have it as a snack.

APPLIN

GRASS · DRAGON
0.2 m
0.5 kg

ABOUT:

It spends its entire life inside an apple. It hides from its natural enemies, bird Pokémon, by pretending it's just an apple and nothing more.

ARCANINE

FIRE
1.9 m
155.0 kg

ABOUT:

The sight of it running over 9978 km in a single day and night has captivated many people.

ARCTOVISH

WATER · ICE
2.0 m
175.0 kg

ABOUT:

Though it's able to capture prey by freezing its surroundings, it has trouble eating the prey afterwards because its mouth is on top of its head.

ARCTOZOLT

ELECTRIC · ICE
2.3 m
150.0 kg

ABOUT:

This Pokémon lived on prehistoric seashores and was able to preserve food with the ice on its body. It went extinct because it moved so slowly.

ARROKUDA

WATER
0.5 m
1.0 kg

ABOUT:

If it sees any movement around it, this Pokémon charges for it straight away, leading with its sharply pointed jaw. It's very proud of that jaw.

BARRASKEWDA

GRASS · DRAGON
1.3 m
30.0 kg

ABOUT:

This Pokémon has a jaw that's as sharp as a spear and as strong as steel. Apparently Barraskewda's flesh is surprisingly tasty, too.

BLASTOISE

WATER
1.6 m
85.5 kg

ABOUT:

Blastoise has water spouts that protrude from its shell. The water spouts are very accurate. They can shoot bullets of water with enough accuracy to strike empty cans from a distance of over 49 m.

BLIPBUG

BUG
0.4 m
8.0 kg

ABOUT:

A constant collector of information, this Pokémon is very smart. Very strong is what it isn't.

BOLTUND

ELECTRIC
1.0 m
34.0 kg

ABOUT:

This Pokémon generates electricity and channels it into its legs to keep them going strong. Boltund can run non-stop for three full days.

BULBASAUR

GRASS
0.7 m
6.9 kg

ABOUT:

Bulbasaur can be seen napping in bright sunlight. There is a seed on its back. By soaking up the sun's rays, the seed grows progressively larger.

BUTTERFREE

BUG · FLYING
1.1 m
32.0 kg

ABOUT:

In battle, it flaps its wings at great speed to release highly toxic dust into the air.

CARKOL

ROCK · FIRE
1.1 m
78.0 kg

ABOUT:

It forms coal inside its body. Coal dropped by this Pokémon once helped fuel the lives of people in the Galar region.

CENTISKORCH

FIRE · BUG
3.0 m
120.0 kg

ABOUT:

While its burning body is already dangerous on its own, this excessively hostile Pokémon also has large and very sharp fangs.

CHARIZARD

FIRE · FLYING
1.7 m
90.5 kg

ABOUT:

It spits fire that is hot enough to melt boulders. It may cause forest fires by blowing flames.

CHARJABUG

BUG · ELECTRIC
0.5 m
10.5 kg

ABOUT:

While its durable shell protects it from attacks, Charjabug strikes at enemies with jolts of electricity discharged from the tips of its jaws.

CHARMANDER

FIRE
0.6 m
8.5 kg

ABOUT:

It has a preference for hot things. When it rains, steam is said to spout from the tip of its tail.

CHARMELEON

FIRE
1.1 m
19.0 kg

ABOUT:

It has a barbaric nature. In battle, it whips its fiery tail around and slashes away with sharp claws.

CHEWTLE

WATER
0.3 m
8.5 kg

ABOUT:

It starts off battles by attacking with its rock-hard horn, but as soon as the opponent flinches, this Pokémon bites down and never lets go.

CINDERACE

FIRE
1.4 m
33.0 kg

ABOUT:

It's skilled at both offence and defence, and it gets pumped up when cheered on. But if it starts showboating, it could put itself in a tough spot.

CLOBBOPUS

FIGHTING
0.6 m
4.0 kg

ABOUT:

Its tentacles tear off easily, but it isn't alarmed when that happens – it knows they'll grow back. It's about as smart as a three-year-old.

COALOSSAL

ROCK · FIRE
2.8 m
310.5 kg

ABOUT:

While it's engaged in battle, its mountain of coal will burn bright red, sending off sparks that scorch the surrounding area.

COPPERAJAH

STEEL
3.0 m
650.0 kg

ABOUT:

These Pokémon live in herds. Their trunks have incredible grip strength, strong enough to crush giant rocks into powder.

GALARIAN CORSOLA

GHOST
0.6 m
0.5 kg

ABOUT:

Sudden climate change wiped out this ancient kind of Corsola. This Pokémon absorbs others' life-force through its branches.

CORVIKNIGHT

FLYING · STEEL
2.2 m
75.0 kg

ABOUT:

With their great intellect and flying skills, these Pokémon very successfully act as the Galar region's airborne taxi service.

CORVISQUIRE

FLYING
0.8 m
16.0 kg

ABOUT:

Smart enough to use tools in battle, these Pokémon have been seen picking up rocks and flinging them or using ropes to wrap up enemies.

CRAMORANT

FLYING · WATER
0.8 m
18.0 kg

ABOUT:

This hungry Pokémon swallows Arrokuda whole. Occasionally, it makes a mistake and tries to swallow a Pokémon other than its preferred prey.

CUFANT

STEEL
1.2 m
100.0 kg

ABOUT:

If a job requires serious strength, this Pokémon will excel at it. Its copper body tarnishes in the rain, turning a vibrant green colour.

CURSOLA

GHOST
1.0 m
0.4 kg

ABOUT:

Be cautious of the ectoplasmic body surrounding its soul. You'll become stiff as stone if you touch it.

GALARIAN DARMANITAN

ICE
1.7 m
120.0 kg

ABOUT:

On days when blizzards blow through, it comes down to where people live. It stashes food in the snowball on its head, taking it home for later.

GALARIAN DARUMAKA

ICE
0.7 m
40.0 kg

ABOUT:

It lived in snowy areas for so long that its fire sac cooled off and atrophied. It now has an organ that generates cold instead.

DOTTLER

BUG · PSYCHIC
0.4 m
19.5 kg

ABOUT:

It barely moves, but it's still alive. Hiding in its shell without food or water seems to have awakened its psychic powers.

DRACOVISH

WATER · DRAGON
2.3 m
215.0 kg

ABOUT:

Its mighty legs are capable of running at speeds exceeding 40 mph, but this Pokémon can't breathe unless it's underwater.

DRACOZOLT

ELECTRIC · DRAGON
1.8 m
190.0 kg

ABOUT:

The powerful muscles in its tail generate its electricity. Compared to its lower body, its upper half is entirely too small.

DRAGAPULT

DRAGON · GHOST
3.0 m
50.0 kg

ABOUT:

When it isn't battling, it keeps Dreepy in the holes on its horns. Once a fight starts, it launches the Dreepy like supersonic missiles.

DRAKLOAK

DRAGON · GHOST
1.4 m
11.0 kg

ABOUT:

It's capable of flying faster than 120 mph. It battles alongside Dreepy and dotes on them until they successfully evolve.

DREDNAW

WATER · ROCK
1.0 m
115.5 kg

ABOUT:

With jaws that can shear through steel rods, this highly aggressive Pokémon chomps down on its unfortunate prey.

DREEPY

DRAGON · GHOST
0.5 m
2.0 kg

ABOUT:

After being reborn as a ghost Pokémon, Dreepy wanders the areas it used to inhabit back when it was alive in prehistoric seas.

DRIZZILE

WATER
0.7 m
11.5 kg

ABOUT:

Highly intelligent, but also very lazy, it keeps enemies out of its territory by laying traps everywhere.

DUBWOOL

NORMAL
1.3 m
43.0 kg

ABOUT:

Weave a carpet from its springy wool, and you end up with something closer to a trampoline. You'll start to bounce the moment you set foot on it.

DURALUDON

STEEL · DRAGON
1.8 m
40.0 kg

ABOUT:

The special metal that composes its body is very light, so this Pokémon has considerable agility. It lives in caves because it dislikes the rain.

EEVEE

NORMAL
0.3 m
6.5 kg

ABOUT:

Thanks to its unstable genetic make-up, this special Pokémon conceals many different possible Evolutions.

EISCUE

ICE
1.4 m
89.0 kg

ABOUT:

This Pokémon keeps its heat-sensitive head cool with ice. It fishes for its food, dangling its single hair into the sea to lure in prey.

ELDEGOSS

GRASS
0.5 m
2.5 kg

ABOUT:

The cotton on the head of this Pokémon can be spun into a glossy, gorgeous yarn – a Galar-regional speciality.

ESPEON

PSYCHIC
0.9 m
26.5 kg

ABOUT:

It unleashes psychic power from the orb on its forehead. When its power is exhausted, the orb grows dull and dark.

LEGENDARY

ETERNATUS

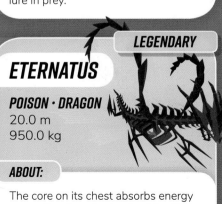

POISON · DRAGON
20.0 m
950.0 kg

ABOUT:

The core on its chest absorbs energy emanating from the lands of the Galar region. This energy is what allows Eternatus to stay active.

FALINKS

FIGHTING
3.0 m
62.0 kg

ABOUT:

The six of them work together as one Pokémon. Teamwork is also their battle strategy, and they constantly change their formation as they fight.

GALARIAN FARFETCH'D

FIGHTING
0.8 m
42.0 kg

ABOUT:

The Farfetch'd of the Galar region are brave warriors, and they wield thick, tough leeks in battle.

FLAPPLE

GRASS · DRAGON
0.3 m
1.0 kg

ABOUT:

It flies on wings of apple skin and spits a powerful acid. It can also change its shape into that of an apple.

FLAREON

FIRE
0.9 m
25.0 kg

ABOUT:

It stores some of the air it inhales in its internal flame pouch, which heats it to almost 150 °C .

FROSMOTH

ICE · BUG
1.3 m
42.0 kg

ABOUT:

It shows no mercy to any who desecrate fields and mountains. It will fly around on its icy wings, causing a blizzard to chase offenders away.

GALVANTULA

BUG · ELECTRIC
0.8 m
14.3 kg

ABOUT:

It lays traps of electrified threads near the nests of bird Pokémon, aiming to snare chicks that are not yet good at flying.

GARCHOMP

DRAGON · GROUND
1.9 m
95.0 kg

ABOUT:

It flies at speeds equal to a jet fighter plane. It never allows its prey to escape.

GASTLY

GHOST · POISON
1.3 m
0.1 kg

ABOUT:

With its gas-like body, it can sneak into any place it desires. However, it can be blown away by wind.

GENGAR

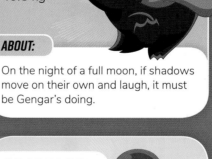

GHOST · POISON
1.5 m
40.5 kg

ABOUT:

On the night of a full moon, if shadows move on their own and laugh, it must be Gengar's doing.

GLACEON

ICE
0.8 m
25.9 kg

ABOUT:

Any who become captivated by the beauty of the snowfall that Glaceon creates will be frozen before they know it.

GOSSIFLEUR

GRASS
0.4 m
2.2 kg

ABOUT:

It anchors itself in the ground with its single leg, then basks in the sun. After absorbing enough sunlight, its petals spread as it blooms brilliantly.

GRAPPLOCT

FIGHTING
1.6 m
39.0 kg

ABOUT:

A body made up of nothing but muscle makes the grappling moves this Pokémon performs with its tentacles tremendously powerful.

GREEDENT

NORMAL
0.6 m
6.0 kg

ABOUT:

Common throughout the Galar region, this Pokémon has strong teeth and can chew through the toughest of berry shells.

GRENINJA

WATER · DARK
1.5 m
40.0 kg

ABOUT:

It appears and vanishes with a ninja's grace. It toys with its enemies using swift movements, while slicing them with throwing stars of sharpest water.

GRIMMSNARL

DARK · FAIRY
1.5 m
61.0 kg

ABOUT:

With the hair wrapped around its body helping to enhance its muscles, this Pokémon can overwhelm even Machamp.

GROOKEY

GRASS
0.3 m
5.0 kg

ABOUT:

It attacks with rapid beats of its stick. As it strikes with amazing speed, it gets more and more pumped.

GROWLITHE

FIRE
0.7 m
19.0 kg

ABOUT:

Extremely loyal, it will fearlessly bark at any opponent to protect its own Trainer from harm.

GRUBBIN

BUG
0.4 m
4.4 kg

ABOUT:

It uses its big jaws to dig nests into the forest floor, and it loves to feed on sweet tree sap.

GYARADOS

WATER · FLYING
6.5 m
235.0 kg

ABOUT:

Once it begins to rampage, a Gyarados will burn everything down, even in a harsh storm.

HATENNA

PSYCHIC
0.4 m
3.4 kg

ABOUT:

If this Pokémon senses a strong emotion, it will run away as fast as it can. It prefers areas without people.

HATTERENE

PSYCHIC · FAIRY
2.1 m
5.1 kg

ABOUT:

If you're too loud around it, you risk being torn apart by the claws on its tentacle. This Pokémon is also known as the Forest Witch.

HATTREM

PSYCHIC
0.6 m
4.8 kg

ABOUT:

Using the braids on its head, it pummels foes to get them to quiet down. One blow from those braids would knock out a professional boxer.

HAUNTER

GHOST · POISON
1.6 m
0.1 kg

ABOUT:

If you get the feeling of being watched in darkness when nobody is around, Haunter is there.

IMPIDIMP

DARK · FAIRY
0.4 m
5.5 kg

ABOUT:

It sneaks into people's homes, stealing things and feasting on the negative energy of the frustrated occupants.

INDEEDEE

PSYCHIC · NORMAL
0.9 m
28.0 kg

ABOUT:

Through its horns, it can pick up on the emotions of creatures around it. Positive emotions are the source of its strength.

INTELEON

WATER
1.9 m
45.2 kg

ABOUT:

It has many hidden capabilities, such as fingertips that can shoot water and a membrane on its back that it can use to glide through the air.

IVYSAUR

GRASS · POISON
1.0 m
13.0 kg

ABOUT:

There is a bud on this Pokémon's back. To support its weight, Ivysaur's legs and trunk grow thick and strong. If it starts spending more time lying in the sunlight, it's a sign that the bud will bloom into a large flower soon.

JOLTEON

ELECTRIC
0.8 m
24.5 kg

ABOUT:

If it is angered or startled, the fur all over its body bristles like sharp needles that pierce foes.

JOLTIK

BUG · ELECTRIC
0.1 m
0.6 kg

ABOUT:

Joltik latch on to other Pokémon and suck out static electricity. They're often found sticking to Yamper's hindquarters.

KUBFU

FIGHTING
0,6 m
12,0 kg

ABOUT:

Kubfu trains hard to perfect its moves. The moves it masters will determine which form it takes when it evolves.

LEAFEON

GRASS
1.0 m
25.5 kg

ABOUT:

Galarians favour the distinctive aroma that drifts from this Pokémon's leaves. There's a popular perfume made using that scent.

GALARIAN LINOONE

DARK · NORMAL
0.5 m
32.5 kg

ABOUT:

It uses its long tongue to taunt opponents. Once the opposition is enraged, this Pokémon hurls itself at the opponent, tackling them forcefully.

LUCARIO

FIGHTING · STEEL
1.2 m
54.0 kg

ABOUT:

It can tell what people are thinking. Only Trainers who have justice in their hearts can earn this Pokémon's trust.

LUDICOLO

WATER · GRASS
1.5 m
55.0 kg

ABOUT:

If it hears festive music, it begins moving in rhythm in order to amplify its power.

MAGIKARP

WATER
0.9 m
10.0 kg

ABOUT:

This weak and pathetic Pokémon gets easily pushed along rivers when there are strong currents.

MEOWTH

NORMAL
0.4 m
4.2 kg

ABOUT:

It washes its face regularly to keep the coin on its forehead spotless. It doesn't get along with Galarian Meowth.

GALARIAN MEOWTH

STEEL
0.4 m
7.5 kg

ABOUT:

Living with a savage, seafaring people has toughened this Pokémon's body so much that parts of it have turned to iron.

MEW

PSYCHIC
0.4 m
4.0 kg

ABOUT:

Mew is said to possess the genetic composition of all Pokémon. It is capable of making itself invisible at will, so it entirely avoids notice even if it approaches people.

MEWTWO

PSYCHIC
2.0 m
122.0 kg

ABOUT:

Mewtwo is a Pokémon that was created by genetic manipulation. However, even though the scientific power of humans created this Pokémon's body, they failed to endow Mewtwo with a compassionate heart.

MILCERY

FAIRY
0.2 m
0.3 kg

ABOUT:

This Pokémon was born from sweet-smelling particles in the air. Its body is made of cream.

MORGREM

DARK · FAIRY
0.8 m
12.5 kg

ABOUT:

With sly cunning, it tries to lure people into the woods. Some believe it to have the power to make crops grow.

MORPEKO

ELECTRIC · DARK
0.3 m
3.0 kg

ABOUT:

As it eats the seeds stored up in its pocket-like pouches, this Pokémon is not just satisfying its constant hunger. It's also generating electricity.

GALARIAN MR. MIME

ICE · PSYCHIC
1.4 m
56.8 kg

ABOUT:

It can radiate chilliness from the bottoms of its feet. It'll spend the whole day tap-dancing on a frozen floor.

MR. RIME

ICE · PSYCHIC
1.5 m
58.2 kg

ABOUT:

Its amusing movements make it very popular. It releases its psychic power from the pattern on its belly.

NICKIT

DARK
0.6 m
8.9 kg

ABOUT:

Aided by the soft pads on its feet, it silently raids the food stores of other Pokémon. It survives off its ill-gotten gains.

NINETALES

FIRE
1.1 m
19.9 kg

ABOUT:

It is said to live 1,000 years, and each of its tails is loaded with supernatural powers.

OBSTAGOON

DARK · NORMAL
1.6 m
46.0 kg

ABOUT:

It evolved after experiencing numerous fights. While crossing its arms, it lets out a shout that would make any opponent flinch.

ORBEETLE

BUG · PSYCHIC
0.4 m
40.8 kg

ABOUT:

It's famous for its high level of intelligence, and the large size of its brain is proof that it also possesses immense psychic power.

PERRSERKER

STEEL
0.8 m
28.0 kg

ABOUT:

What appears to be an iron helmet is actually hardened hair. This Pokémon lives for the thrill of battle.

PICHU

ELECTRIC
0.3 m
2.0 kg

ABOUT:

Despite its small size, it can zap even adult humans. However, if it does so, it also surprises itself.

PIKACHU

ELECTRIC
0.4 m
6.0 kg

ABOUT:

When Pikachu meet, they'll touch their tails together and exchange electricity through them as a form of greeting.

PINCURCHIN

ELECTRIC
0.3 m
1.0 kg

ABOUT:

It feeds on seaweed, using its teeth to scrape it off rocks. Electric current flows from the tips of its spines.

POLTEAGEIST

GHOST
0.2 m
0.4 kg

ABOUT:

Leaving leftover black tea unattended is asking for this Pokémon to come along and pour itself into it, turning the tea into a new Polteageist.

GALARIAN PONYTA

PSYCHIC
1.0 m
30.0 kg

ABOUT:

Its small horn hides a healing power. With a few rubs from this Pokémon's horn, any slight wound you have will be healed.

PSYDUCK

PSYCHIC
0.4 m
4.0 kg

ABOUT:

If it uses its mysterious power, Psyduck can't remember having done so. It apparently can't form a memory of such an event because it goes into an altered state that is much like deep sleep.

RABOOT

FIRE
0.6 m
9.0 kg

ABOUT:

Its thick and fluffy fur protects it from the cold and enables it to use hotter fire moves.

RAICHU

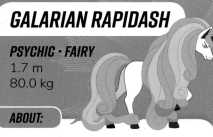

ELECTRIC
0.8 m
30.0 kg

ABOUT:

Its long tail serves as a ground to protect itself from its own high-voltage power.

GALARIAN RAPIDASH

PSYCHIC · FAIRY
1.7 m
80.0 kg

ABOUT:

Brave and prideful, this Pokémon dashes airily through the forest, its steps aided by the psychic power stored in the fur on its fetlocks.

RILLABOOM

GRASS
2.1 m
90.0 kg

ABOUT:

The one with the best drumming techniques becomes the boss of the troop. It has a gentle disposition and values harmony among its group.

RIOLU

FIGHTING
0.7 m
20.2 kg

ABOUT:

It's exceedingly energetic, with enough stamina to keep running all through the night. Taking it for walks can be a challenging experience.

ROLYCOLY

ROCK
0.3 m
12.0 kg

ABOUT:

Most of its body has the same composition as coal. Fittingly, this Pokémon was first discovered in coal mines about 400 years ago.

ROOKIDEE

FLYING
0.2 m
1.8 kg

ABOUT:
It will bravely challenge any opponent, no matter how powerful. This Pokémon benefits from every battle – even a defeat increases its strength a bit.

RUNERIGUS

GROUND · GHOST
1.6 m
66.6 kg

ABOUT:
A powerful curse was woven into an ancient painting. After absorbing the spirit of a Yamask, the painting began to move.

SANDACONDA

GROUND
3.8 m
65.5 kg

ABOUT:
Its unique style of coiling allows it to blast sand out of its sand sac more efficiently.

SCORBUNNY

FIRE
0.3 m
4.5 kg

ABOUT:
A warm-up of running around gets fire energy coursing through this Pokémon's body. Once that happens, it's ready to fight at full power.

SILICOBRA

GROUND
2.2 m
7.6 kg

ABOUT:
It spews sand from its nostrils. While the enemy is blinded, it burrows into the ground to hide.

SINISTEA

GHOST
0.1 m
0.2 kg

ABOUT:
This Pokémon is said to have been born when a lonely spirit possessed a cold, leftover cup of tea.

SIRFETCH'D

FIGHTING
0.8 m
117.0 kg

ABOUT:
Only Farfetch'd that have survived many battles can attain this evolution. When this Pokémon's leek withers, it will retire from combat.

SIZZLIPEDE

FIRE · BUG
0.7 m
1.0 kg

ABOUT:
It stores flammable gas in its body and uses it to generate heat. The yellow sections on its belly get particularly hot.

SKWOVET

NORMAL
0.3 m
2.5 kg

ABOUT:
Found throughout the Galar region, this Pokémon becomes uneasy if its cheeks are ever completely empty of berries.

SNOM

ICE · BUG
0.3 m
3.8 kg

ABOUT:
It shows no mercy to any who desecrate fields and mountains. It will fly around on its icy wings, causing a blizzard to chase offenders away.

SNORLAX

NORMAL
2.1 m
460.0 kg

ABOUT:
This Pokémon's stomach is so strong, even eating mouldy or rotten food will not affect it.

SOBBLE

WATER
0.3 m
4.0 kg

ABOUT:
When scared, this Pokémon cries. Its tears pack the chemical punch of 100 onions, and attackers won't be able to resist weeping.

SQUIRTLE

WATER
0.5 m
9.0 kg

ABOUT:

Squirtle's shell is not merely used for protection. The shell's rounded shape and the grooves on its surface help minimize resistance in water, enabling this Pokémon to swim at high speeds.

STONJOURNER

ROCK
2.5 m
520.0 kg

ABOUT:

It stands in grasslands, watching the sun's descent from zenith to horizon. This Pokémon has a talent for delivering dynamic kicks.

GALARIAN STUNFISK

GROUND · STEEL
0.7 m
20.5 kg

ABOUT:

Living in mud with a high iron content has given it a strong steel body.

SYLVEON

FAIRY
1.0 m
23.5 kg

ABOUT:

There's a Galarian fairy tale that describes a beautiful Sylveon vanquishing a dreadful dragon Pokémon.

THIEVUL

DARK
1.2 m
19.9 kg

ABOUT:

It secretly marks potential targets with a scent. By following the scent, it stalks its targets and steals from them when they least expect it.

THWACKEY

GRASS
0.7 m
14.0 kg

ABOUT:

The faster a Thwackey can beat out a rhythm with its two sticks, the more respect it wins from its peers.

TOXEL

ELECTRIC · POISON
0.4 m
11.0 kg

ABOUT:

It stores poison in an internal poison sac and secretes that poison through its skin. If you touch this Pokémon, a tingling sensation follows.

TOXTRICITY

ELECTRIC · POISON
1.6 m
40.0 kg

ABOUT:

Capable of generating 15,000 volts of electricity, this Pokémon looks down on all that would challenge it.

UMBREON

DARK
1.0 m
27.0 kg

ABOUT:

On the night of a full moon, or when it gets excited, the ring patterns on its body glow yellow.

URSHIFU

FIGHTING · DARK
1.9 m
105.0 kg

ABOUT:

This form of Urshifu is a strong believer in the one-hit KO. Its strategy is to leap in close to foes and land a devastating blow with a hardened fist.

VAPOREON

WATER
1.0 m
29.0 kg

ABOUT:

When Vaporeon's fins begin to vibrate, it is a sign that rain will come within a few hours.

VENUSAUR

GRASS · POISON
2.0 m
100.0 kg

ABOUT:

There is a large flower on Venusaur's back. The flower is said to take on vivid colours if it gets plenty of nutrition and sunlight. The flower's aroma soothes the emotions of people.

VULPIX

FIRE
0.6 m
9.9 kg

ABOUT:

While young, it has six gorgeous tails. When it grows, several new tails are sprouted.

WARTORTLE

WATER
1.0 m
22.5 kg

ABOUT:

Its tail is large and covered with a rich, thick fur. The tail becomes increasingly deeper in colour as Wartortle ages. The scratches on its shell are evidence of this Pokémon's toughness as a battler.

GALARIAN WEEZING

POISON · FAIRY
1.1 m
34.0 kg

ABOUT:

This Pokémon consumes particles that contaminate the air. Instead of leaving droppings, it expels clean air.

WOBBUFFET

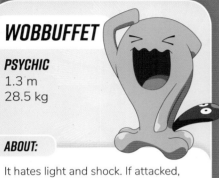

PSYCHIC
1.3 m
28.5 kg

ABOUT:

It hates light and shock. If attacked, it inflates its body to pump up its counterstrike.

WOOLOO

NORMAL
0.6 m
6.0 kg

ABOUT:

Its curly fleece is such an effective cushion that this Pokémon could fall off a cliff and stand right back up at the bottom, unharmed.

GALARIAN YAMASK

GROUND · GHOST
0.5 m
1.5 kg

ABOUT:

It's said that this Pokémon was formed when an ancient clay tablet was drawn to a vengeful spirit.

YAMPER

ELECTRIC
0.3 m
13.5 kg

ABOUT:

This Pokémon is very popular as a herding dog in the Galar region. As it runs, it generates electricity from the base of its tail.

LEGENDARY

ZACIAN

FAIRY · STEEL
2.8 m
355.0 kg

ABOUT:

Able to cut down anything with a single strike, it became known as the Fairy King's Sword, and it inspired awe in friend and foe alike.

LEGENDARY

ZAMAZENTA

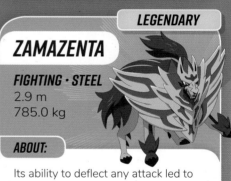

FIGHTING · STEEL
2.9 m
785.0 kg

ABOUT:

Its ability to deflect any attack led to it being known as the Fighting Master's Shield. It was feared and respected by all.

ZARUDE

DARK · GRASS
1.8 m
70.0 kg

ABOUT:

Within dense forests, this Pokémon lives in a pack with others of its kind. It's incredibly aggressive, and the other Pokémon of the forest fear it.

GALARIAN ZIGZAGOON

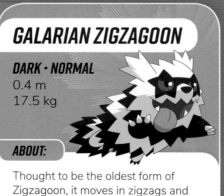

DARK · NORMAL
0.4 m
17.5 kg

ABOUT:

Thought to be the oldest form of Zigzagoon, it moves in zigzags and wreaks havoc upon its surroundings.

ZWEILOUS

DARK · DRAGON
1.4 m
50.0 kg

ABOUT:

Their two heads will fight each other over a single piece of food. Zweilous are covered in scars even without battling others.

SPOT THE DIFFERENCE

You've been gathering Pokémon data – now let's test your spotting skills. **Can you find 8 differences in the second grid?**

GRID 1

WOW!

Some Pokémon that have Galarian forms, such as Meowth and Linoone, also have new Evolution forms. Galarian Meowth can evolve to Perrserker, and Galarian Linoone to Obstagoon!

GRID 2

Colour a Poké Ball for every difference that you spot!

TEAM ROCKET TROUBLE!

Team Rocket has stolen a group of Ivysaur! Someone must catch up with Jessie and James to bring the Ivysaur back to safety - will it be you?

START

| 1 | 2 | 3 | 4 | 5 TEAM ROCKET IS ON THE RUN! JUMP FORWARD 2. | 6 |

| 28 | 27 | 26 | 25 | 24 | 23 | 22 |

29

| 30 | 31 | 32 PIKACHU HAS BEATEN MEOWTH IN BATTLE! MOVE FORWARD 4. | 33 | 34 | 35 | 36 |

| 58 | 57 | 56 | 55 | 54 | 53 YOU'RE LOST IN THE HOENN REGION. MISS A TURN. | 52 |

59

| 60 | 61 | 62 TEAM ROCKET HAS SET A TRAP FOR PIKACHU! GO BACK 2. | 63 | 64 | 65 | 66 |

WHAT TO DO:

- Find some coins to use as counters, and a dice.
- Choose one player to start, and then take turns to roll the dice.
- Move forward the number of spaces shown on the dice. If you land on a square with instructions, follow the directions.
- The first player to reach the Finish is the winner!

For up to 4 players

Look out twerps, we're ready to strike!

7 **8** **9** **10** **11** **12** **13**

14

21 **20** YOU'VE BEEN DISTRACTED BY A NEW GALARIAN POKÉMON. MISS A TURN. **19** **18** **17** TEAM ROCKET HAS BLASTED OFF TO KANTO TO HIDE. GO BACK TO SQUARE 6. **16** **15**

37 **38** **39** **40** **41** **42** **43**

44

45

51 **50** **49** UH-OH, WOBBUFFET USED ITS MIRROR COAT MOVE! MOVE BACK 3. **48** **47** **46**

67 **68** YOU'VE SPOTTED TEAM ROCKET'S DISGUISE. MOVE FORWARD 1. **69** **70** **71** **72** WAY TO GO, YOU SAVED THE IVYSAUR!

FINISH

CAUGHT THE BUG

Chloe is looking over Cerise Laboratory's data on Bug-type Pokémon. **Can you help her find these exact sequences in the grid? Look forward, back and diagonally.**

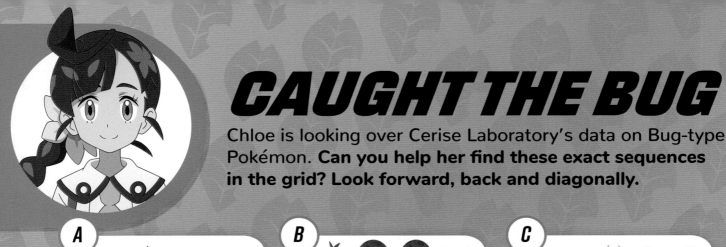

A **B** **C**

Hold on, there's one more Bug-type Pokémon to spot! **Can you see the Butterfree?**

 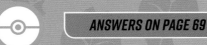

BATTLE MODE!

Which Pokémon are locked in battle? **Follow the lines to find the duelling pairs, then circle who you think will have the edge each time!**

ANSWERS ON PAGE 69

47

I SPY POKÉMON

How many of each Pokémon can you spy on this page? When the counting is done, it's time for some serious colouring!

ANSWERS ON PAGE 69

MAKE A SPLASH

Take a look ... this Water-type Pokémon has become invisible after being soaked with water. **Join the dots to reveal who it is!**

WOW!

Dracovish, captured by Ash in Galar, is a Water- and Dragon-type Fossil Pokémon. It can run at high speeds underwater and has an incredible Ice Fang move!

GOTTA CATCH A WHAT?!

ASH AND GOH ARE ON A JOURNEY THROUGH THE WORLD OF POKÉMON. GOH WANTS TO CATCH ONE OF EVERY KIND OF POKÉMON. HE HAS CAUGHT LOTS SO FAR, BUT WHAT TO CATCH NEXT?

One day, Ash and Goh were eating lunch when Goh realised how cool it was that Ash and his Pikachu were best friends. Right then, he made a decision. "I'm gonna catch ... a Pikachu!!" he proclaimed.

Ash was shocked. Pikachu were hard to find.

Just then, Professor Cerise arrived. "I recently received information about a sighting of an outbreak of Pikachu," he explained. "Since you're research fellows, I was just going to ask you to go have a look."

Chrysa showed them the location on Goh's Rotom Phone. "It's always been a habitat for Pikachu," she said. "But it's unusual for them to gather like this."

Ash and Goh couldn't believe their luck! Moments later, they were on their way.

Goh and Ash soon arrived in a mountain forest in search of the wild Pikachu outbreak. They quickly spotted a lone Pikachu. Goh tried to catch it, but failed. Instead, Goh's Poké Ball hit him in his own face! Just then, a wild Pikachu appeared to check that Goh was all right.

"That Pikachu must love to take care of others," said Ash.

Goh noticed the shape of the wild Pikachu's tail and checked on his Rotom Phone – it was a female Pikachu!

"Hey! You could catch it if you're quick about it!" Ash told Goh.

Goh snapped into action and quickly caught the female Pikachu. As Goh said hello, his Pikachu let off a Thunderbolt and electrocuted Goh! Ash laughed. "That's pretty much how Pikachu say hello. You'll get used to it really fast."

Goh's Pikachu led them to all the other wild Pikachu. They were digging in the rocks nearby. "Wait, are they looking for something?" asked Goh.

Just then, one of the Pikachu found a glowing rock and touched it. The Pikachu transformed!
"Now I understand," said Goh. "When a Pikachu touches a Thunder Stone, it evolves into a Raichu!"
The Pikachu were all gathered here to find the Thunder Stone.

Goh's Pikachu tried to give the Thunder Stone to Ash's Pikachu, but he didn't want it.
"My Pikachu has always wanted to get stronger as a Pikachu," Ash explained. "I think it's the best thing for everyone to evolve when they want to."
Goh's Pikachu decided she didn't want to evolve either, so she gave the Thunder Stone to Goh for safe keeping.

Just then, the Team Rocket trio arrived – Jessie, James and Meowth. They were the bad guys, out to catch any Pokémon they could, especially Ash's Pikachu!

"We'll be assuming control of this pack of Pikachu, if you please!" Jessie announced.

They had a vacuum machine that could suck up and trap all the Pikachu. They started by trapping just one Pikachu to try it out. The Pikachu's Thunderbolt was useless inside the machine.

Ash and Goh couldn't believe it. They had to stop the Team Rocket trio! "Stop it right now!" shouted Ash.

But Jessie summoned the Rocket Prize Master, which gave her access to the whole of Team Rocket's Pokémon stock. It gave them two Pokémon that looked very cute, but turned out to be very good at fighting – the rabbit Pokémon Buneary and the chinchilla Pokémon Minccino. During the battle, Goh used Raboot's Double Kick and Ash used Pikachu's Iron Tail, but they were evenly matched.

Jessie told Buneary to use a Pound move and, in the end, all the Pikachu were captured – including Ash's Pikachu!

The Team Rocket trio disappeared with all the Pikachu. Ash and Goh were left behind in the dust. Then, they noticed Goh's Pikachu had been left behind, too. She was very sad that all her friends were gone. "Let's go save all of them ... together!" Goh exclaimed. And they all ran to find their friends.

They soon found the Team Rocket trio and all the captured Pikachu. "You won't get away this time!" said Goh. "Give those Pikachu back!"

While Ash and Goh battled the bad guys with their Pokémon, Goh's Pikachu sneaked over to her trapped friends and tried to free them, but she couldn't find a way.

Suddenly, Meowth spotted Goh's Pikachu near the machine. He tried to suck her up to join her friends. "Prepare to join all your buddy pals!" Meowth said menacingly.

Goh's Pikachu had an idea. She called for Goh's attention and he quickly realised what she was thinking. He passed her the Thunder Stone just as she disappeared into the machine. To everyone's amazement, the machine's tube grew and grew, and then out exploded a Raichu!

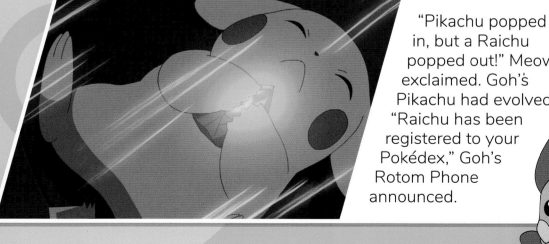

"Pikachu popped in, but a Raichu popped out!" Meowth exclaimed. Goh's Pikachu had evolved. "Raichu has been registered to your Pokédex," Goh's Rotom Phone announced.

A moment later, some other Raichu arrived and they used a combined Thunderbolt to destroy Team Rocket's machine. All the Pikachu were freed!

They stood one on top of the other and created a massive Thunderbolt to blow the bad guys away.

Ash's Pikachu came bounding over.

"Hey, buddy! You're back!" said Ash happily.

Goh's Raichu was pleased to see him, too. They all headed back home, where the professors thanked Ash and Goh for all the new data. "So the Pikachu gathering was all about Thunder Stones? Incredible!" said Professor Cerise.

"I only set out to catch a Pikachu ..." said Goh, watching his new Raichu making lots of new friends.

GOH'S DREAM OF CATCHING EVERY KIND OF POKÉMON IS ONE STEP CLOSER TO BECOMING REALITY, AS THE JOURNEY CONTINUES!

THIS OR THAT POKÉMON

Which Fire-type Pokémon would you choose to catch?
Tick your choice to add it to your Pokédex!

GROWLITHE OR **FLAREON**

SCORBUNNY OR **CHARMANDER**

WOW!

Too hot to handle! A full-power Pyro Ball from a Cinderace is one of the most devastating Fire-type moves there is.

VULPIX OR **RABOOT**

CHARIZARD OR **CINDERACE**

PIKACHU, IRON TAIL!

Join the dots to prepare for an awesome battle! Then colour the picture.

Cross out all the matching letter pairs and rearrange the remaining letters to reveal one of Pikachu's winning moves!

P T B E A M U A L C O Y D
M K R I Y C I P T K N H

T _ _ _ _ _ _ _ _ T

POKÉ BALL POPS

Snack in style with these awesome cake pops!
Ask an adult to help.

WHAT YOU'LL NEED:

- A baked cake
- 170g soft cream cheese
- Lollipop sticks
- Red and white candy buttons
- Black icing pen
- Mini white chocolate drops

1

- Crumble the cake into a large bowl and add the cream cheese. Mix to form a dough.

2

- Roll the dough into small balls and place in the fridge for one hour.

3

- Melt some white candy buttons and dip in the end of a lollipop stick. Push the stick halfway into a chilled ball and lay down to set. Repeat with more sticks and balls.

4

- Dip the balls fully into the rest of the melted white candy, tap to let the excess drip, and then let them set for one hour.

5

- Melt the red candy buttons and dip in your white cake pops halfway. Again, let them set.

6

- Pipe a thin line of black icing across the middle of each cake pop and place a white chocolate drop in the centre.

TIP:

Poke small holes into a cardboard box so you can stand up your cake pops as they dry.

LIGHTNING-QUICK CHALLENGE

Professor Cerise has given you list of Pokémon to catch, but it's a battle against the clock! **Set a timer and tick the Pokémon as you spot them.**

1. GROOKEY	✓
2. SCORBUNNY	✓
3. SOBBLE	✓
4. GOSSIFLEUR	✓
5. ELDEGOSS	✓
6. WOOLOO	✓
7. CORVIKNIGHT	✓
8. DREDNAW	✓
9. ALCREMIE	✓
10. YAMPER	✓
11. MORPEKO	✓
12. CRAMORANT	✓

How long did it take you to find them all?

2 MINS

ANSWERS ON PAGE 69

DISCOVER A POKÉMON

Ash and Goh have a blast finding Pokémon, and now it's your turn! **Imagine a new rare type of Pokémon that you might discover, and share your findings here.**

WHERE DID YOU DISCOVER THE POKÉMON?

DOES IT HAVE A SIGNATURE MOVE?

WHAT ARE ITS EVOLUTIONS?

WHICH POKÉMON WOULD IT DEFEAT IN BATTLE?

Fill in this information for your Pokédex.

HEIGHT:

WEIGHT:

CATEGORY:

ABILITIES:

TYPE:

WEAKNESSES:

Draw your Pokémon inside the Poké Ball!

ROTOM RIDDLES

Can you help Goh decipher this Rotom data?
Solve the clues and write the Pokémon names.

A brown fox-like Pokémon.
It survives by stealing food from others.

A Pokémon whose name begins with 'A'.
It has an orange body marked with black stripes.

This Pokémon keeps its head cool with ice.
Its body resembles a penguin.

This Pokémon can tell what others are thinking.
It evolves from a Riolu.

A Galarian Pokémon with a strong steel body.
It lives in mud.

A Fire-type Pokémon that has six tails when it is young.
It can evolve into a Ninetales.

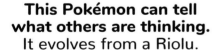

A purple Ghost- and Poison-type Pokémon.
It can evolve into a Gengar.

This Pokémon's name begins with 'M'.
It lives in the river and is pushed along by currents.

This Pokémon evolves from a Raboot.
It has strong legs and can kick fireballs at opponents.

A Flying-type Pokémon that can spit fire. It evolves from a Charmeleon.

This Pokémon's body is made of cream. It is a white, Fairy-type Pokémon.

It's time to level up the challenge!
Can you fit your Pokémon names into this puzzle?

Unscramble the circled letters.
Which mystery Pokémon is revealed?

_ _ _ _ _ _ _ _

ANSWERS ON PAGE 69

THE ULTIMATE TRAINER TEST

Professor Cerise has set a quiz to test your Pokémon knowledge. Have you mastered all you need to know, or do you have more training to do?

WORK YOUR WAY UP FROM BEGINNER TO MASTER.

TIP:
Look back through this Annual if you get stuck.

BEGINNER — Tick your answer.

TRUE OR FALSE?

	TRUE	FALSE
1. PIKACHU IS A FIRE-TYPE POKÉMON.		✓
2. THWACKEY EVOLVES FROM GROOKEY.	✓	
3. EEVEE IS CHLOE'S PARTNER.	✓	
4. RIOLU CAN EVOLVE INTO CHARIZARD.		✓
5. MEOWTH HAS A GALARIAN FORM.	✓	

INTERMEDIATE — Circle your answer.

1. GALVANTULA IS A DUAL-TYPE POKÉMON. WHAT ARE ITS TWO TYPES?	(BUG AND ELECTRIC) OR	BUG AND POISON
2. IN WHICH REGION WILL YOU FIND A NICKIT?	KANTO OR	GALAR
3. HOW MANY ARMS DOES A MACHAMP HAVE?	(FOUR) OR	SIX
4. CAN A SNORLAX DYNAMAX?	YES OR	NO
5. FROM WHICH POKÉMON DOES A GYARADOS EVOLVE?	STUNFISK OR	(MAGIKARP)

MASTER

Write your answer.

1. **WHAT WEAPON DOES A GALARIAN FARFETCH'D WIELD IN BATTLE?**

   a   Leek

2. **WHICH BLUE POKÉMON CRIES WHEN IT'S SCARED?**

   Sobble

3. **WHAT SHAPE OF MARK DOES A WOOBAT LEAVE BEHIND?**

   Heart

4. **FROM WHICH POKÉMON DOES A GRAPPLOCT EVOLVE?**

   clobus

5. **WHAT'S THE NAME OF THE WATER- AND DRAGON-TYPE FOSSIL POKÉMON?**

   draco vish

Add up your correct answers. How many did you get right?

10/10

ANSWERS ON PAGE 69

ANSWERS

PAGE 7

It's All About Mew
Pages: 11, 12, 22, 37, 45, 46, 61, & 67

PAGES 8-9

Who's That Pokémon?
A – Stunfisk, **B** – Butterfree, **C** – Zigzagoon,
D – Nickit

Poké Ball – Go!

1. Kubfu, **2.** Farfetch'd, **3.** Dracovish, **4.** Ponyta,
5. Skwovet, **6.** Corviknight

PAGES 12-13

Hide 'n' Sneak

WEELTCH — CHEWTLE
AREECMIL — ALCREMIE
AWDDREN — DREDNAW
ORCHSKITENC — CENTISKORCH
RESREPREKR — PERRSERKER
BUYNNROCS — SCORBUNNY

Pixel Puzzle
1. Cramorant, **2.** Rillaboom, **3.** Zamazenta

In a Spin
CINDERACE

PAGES 14-15

Gigantamax Wordsearch

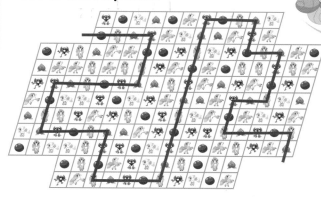

The Gigantic Pokémon is Eternatus.
'Snorlax' appears 7 times.

PAGES 24-25

Race to the Rapidash

Eev-olved or Not?
Inteleon

PAGE 28

Go, Go, Grass Types!
A. Lotad
B. Bulbasaur
C. Thwackey
D. Lombre
E. Appletun

PAGES 42-43

Spot the Difference

PAGE 46

Caught the Bug

PAGE 47

Battle Mode!
Pikachu and Tyranitar
Blastoise and Venusaur
Lucario and Dragonite
Gengar and Meowth

PAGE 48

I Spy Pokémon

8   5   8   6   6

PAGE 59

Pikachu, Iron Tail!
THUNDERBOLT

PAGE 61

Lightning-Quick Challenge

PAGES 64-65

Rotom Riddles
The mystery Pokémon is Pikachu.

		V				H							M
		U				U							A
	L	U	C	A	R	I	O						G
		P				N							I
		I				T							K
		X		S	T	U	N	F	I	S	K		A
						E							R
C	I	N	D	E	R	A	C	E					P
I						R							
C						C		E					
K			C	H	A	R	I	Z	A	R	D		
I						A		S					
T				M	I	L	C	E	R	Y			
						N		U					
						E		E					

PAGES 66-67

The Ultimate Trainer Test

Beginner
1. False, **2.** True, **3.** True, **4.** False, **5.** True

Intermediate
1. Bug and electric, **2.** Galar, **3.** Four, **4.** Yes, **5.** Magikarp

Master
1. Leek, **2.** Sobble, **3.** Heart, **4.** Clobbopus, **5.** Dracovish